Mathematics Games

John Deft

Head of Mathematics
St Brendan's Sixth Form College
Bristol

First published 1987

Published by
MACMILLAN EDUCATION LTD
Houndmills, Basingstoke, Hampshire RG21 2XS
and London
Companies and representatives
throughout the world

Typeset by Vine & Gorfin Ltd, Exmouth, Devon
Printed in Hong Kong

British Library Cataloguing in Publication Data
Deft, John
Mathematics games.
1. Mathematics – Study and teaching
2. Educational games
I. Title
510'7'8   QA19.G3
ISBN 0-333-43550-8

CONTENTS

INTRODUCTION

Many teachers have come to recognise in recent years – as others have known all along – that appropriate games have a contribution to make to the mathematical education of children. Such games, used as part of a balanced curriculum, can bring substantial benefits to the children who play them, in terms both of the enjoyment and interest they arouse and of the actual learning that takes place as the games proceed.

Games like the ones in this book can be used in a variety of ways. Some teachers playing mathematics games for the first time may wish to introduce them initially in the 'Maths Club' or a similar group, but they have their place in 'ordinary' lessons too. Some games are particularly suitable as an introduction to a new topic, while others are ideal when revision of a topic is needed. Some games can act as starting points for investigations or other project work, and others again can usefully fill ten minutes at the end of a lesson or provide some variety in a lesson consisting mainly (as occasional lessons inevitably must) of formal written work.

The games are organised in five sections, but this is mainly for ease of reading, and most of the games can be adapted for numbers or situations other than those suggested. The description of each game begins with a suggested age range, but this too is for guidance only, and teachers may well find that older or younger pupils get something worthwhile out of the game as well. Teachers must decide, in any case, which games are most likely to be successful with particular groups.

The second part of each game description indicates the mathematical topics or ideas which are chiefly associated with the game. In a few cases these are particular skills which are needed beforehand, but in general the games can be played by pupils without specific mathematical knowledge, as long as they are willing and able to 'think mathematically', whatever that might mean! As a guide to teachers who want to relate a game to a particular topic, however, a short content index is provided on

page 120. This should not be seen as definitive – many games can be adapted to suit the particular players involved – but may be of some help when time is short.
Ready . . . Steady . . .

GAMES FOR ONE PLAYER

The games - or perhaps we should call them puzzles - in this section require a pupil to perform some task given at the outset, and no other person need normally be involved. However, the greatest benefits will usually be derived if pupils are allowed - even encouraged - to discuss their proposed solutions with one another as they work.

Mazes

Age range 9 to 13

Mathematics Spatial skills

Equipment Prepared mazes; squared paper

Method of play

Initially, each pupil is given a prepared maze and asked to find a way through it. Pupils are then invited to design their own mazes on squared paper. The following (optional) rules may be helpful:

1 The size of the mazes should be about 10 × 10 squares; there should be one entrance and one exit.
2 There should be just one route (not counting any retracing of steps) from the entrance to the exit.
3 Every part of the maze should be accessible; no part should be wholly surrounded by walls.

Notes

Having designed their mazes, pupils should try them out on one another. As a variation, a pupil may be given a copy of a maze and asked to *describe* in words the route to be followed.

Example

The maze on the opposite page may be used as an example.

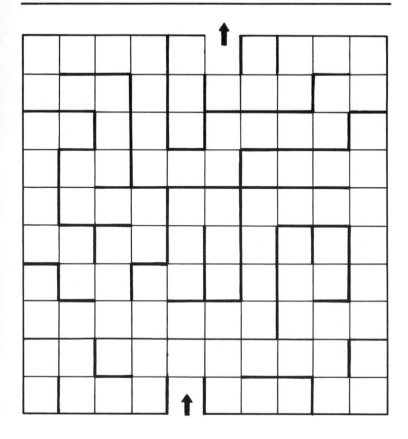

Tower of Hanoi

Age range   9 to 14

Mathematics   Problem-solving skills

Equipment   Three spikes and five discs, as described below.

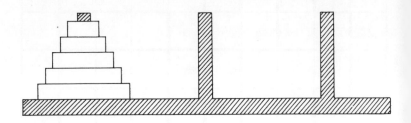

Method of play

The game begins with all five discs placed in order of size on the
first spike, and the object is to move them all to the last spike.
The rules of movement are as follows:

1 Only one disc may be moved at a time.

2 A move consists of taking the top disc from any spike and
  placing it as the top disc on any other spike.

3 A larger disc may never be placed on top of a smaller one.

Solution

With five discs, the game can be completed in 31 moves. If the
spikes are labelled L, C and R, and the discs are numbered 1 to
5 in order of increasing size, a possible sequence is 1R, 2C, 1C,
3R, 1L, 2R, 1R, 4C, 1C, 2L, 1L, 3C, 1R, 2C, 1C, 5R, 1L, 2R, 1R,
3L, 1C, 2L, 1L, 4R, 1R, 2C, 1C, 3R, 1L, 2R, 1R.

Notes

The game can be made longer (but little harder) by increasing
the number of discs, or shorter by decreasing it; n discs involve a
minimum of $2^n - 1$ moves. According to legend, there is an Indian

monastery which has a 64-disc 'Tower of Hanoi', where the monks sit all day patiently transferring discs from one spike to another; at the moment that they make the last transfer, the end of the world will occur. Pupils may care to work out how soon that can be expected to happen!

It is much the most satisfactory arrangement to have spikes and discs made of plastic or wood, and the Craft Department may well be able to help out. As a temporary measure, however, the discs can be cut from card or even paper, and the spikes can be replaced by three circles on a fixed base.

Anagrams

Age range   9 to 16

Mathematics   As required

Equipment   Pencil and paper

Method of play

Pupils are first introduced to the idea of an anagram, using the examples below if necessary. Each pupil then makes up anagrams of ten words commonly used in mathematics (or in a particular area of mathematics) and gives these anagrams to another pupil to solve. Initially, the anagrams will almost certainly be mere jumbles of letters; abler pupils may later be able to form real words or phrases, or fictitious names of mathematicians.

Examples

Polygons   QUEARS, LALALAPREGORM, OGENHAX, GNOOBL
Metric units   MARG, DENSOC, LILILIMERT, TRENTICMET
Trigonometry   ENIS, ESCOIN, PSYTENOUHE, STANECCO
Words and phrases   TEACHER, INTEGRAL, MILKO TREE, SO ICELESS
'Mathematicians'   A. BARGEL, C. BATTRUS, FINN O'TUC, G.O. DANCE

Answers

square, parallelogram, hexagon, oblong
gram, second, millilitre, centimetre
sine, cosine, hypotenuse, cosecant
hectare, triangle, kilometre, isosceles
algebra, subtract, function, decagon

Frogs

Age range   9 upwards

Mathematics   Problem-solving skills

Equipment   A grid (as shown below) and six counters or coins

Method of play

The game begins with three black counters on the first three squares of the grid, and three white counters on the last three squares. Alternatively, coins set respectively to 'heads' and 'tails' may be used.

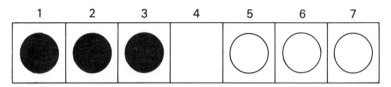

The object of the game is to make the black and the white counters change places, according to these two rules.

1 Only one counter may be moved at a time.

2 A counter may be moved *either* by sliding it into an empty square immediately adjacent *or* by jumping it over one other counter (of either colour) into an empty square immediately beyond.

Solution

The game as described can be completed in fifteen moves; one possible 'shortest solution' consists of moving the counters in squares 5, 3, 2, 4, 6, 7, 5, 3, 1, 2, 4, 6, 5, 3, and 4.

Variations

There are several obvious variations: four counters (two of each colour) on a five-square grid, for example, or eight counters on a nine-square grid. Older pupils might carry out an extended investigation into the relationship between the number of counters and the minimum number of moves required.

Cross-number Puzzles

Age range   9 upwards

Mathematics   Arithmetic and/or algebra as required

Equipment   Prepared puzzles and clues

Method of play

Initially, pupils may be given the prepared puzzle grids and the accompanying clues, and invited to complete them. As a further activity, pupils may be asked to compile their own puzzles for solution by other pupils.

Notes

There are essentially four kinds of cross-number clue, although there can be some overlap between them. The simplest type of clue is the straightforward arithmetical calculation: for example, the clue '37×5' leads directly to the answer 185, which can be entered at once in the appropriate squares of the grid. Clues of this type can usually be solved quite easily by any pupil with a reasonable grasp of arithmetic, assisted if necessary by a pocket calculator.

A second type of clue requires the recall of items of mathematical or general knowledge – for example, 'the number of pounds in a hundredweight' or 'the year of the Battle of Hastings'. Such clues must obviously be suited to the age and experience of the pupils concerned, and mathematical tables or other reference books should be to hand.

Thirdly there is the indirect clue such as 'the square of (**f** across)'. If the answer to (**f** across) is already known there is obviously no problem, but this too may be defined indirectly. Even more obscure is the fourth type of clue, which consists merely of a vague hint such as 'an even number'. Clues of this type are normally solved by referring to the shape of the grid and to any checked figures, as well as to any reference to this answer in other clues. For example, if (**b** down) has two figures and is 'a prime number', and (**d** across), which has three figures starting with a 2, is 'the square of (**b** down)' it is not hard to deduce that (**d** across) is 289 and (**b** down) is 17.

The grid is normally square or rectangular; for cross-number puzzles at secondary school level a suitable size is probably between 6×6 and 9×9 squares. The black squares are normally placed so as to give the grid either bilateral or rotational symmetry, but this is for aesthetic rather than mathematical reasons. All the numbers should be interlinked (rather than allowing the white part of each grid to fall into two or more separate parts), and at least half the figures in each number should be checked – that is, they should be shared with another number. None of these rules are mandatory, but they are accepted by most crossword and cross-number compilers as leading to better and more satisfying puzzles.

The two sample puzzles which follow illustrate some of the possibilities. Puzzle A relies mainly on direct arithmetic, and is probably suitable for an average eleven-year-old, while Puzzle B makes much more use of indirect clues and hints and is likely to challenge even able sixth-form students.

Answers

3	4	5	7	■	1	■
9	■	7	■	3	7	5
0	■	6	8	5	2	■
2	1	■	4	■	8	1
■	3	5	0	1	■	2
7	2	0	■	9	■	2
■	9	■	2	6	4	5

9	6	1	6	4	4
6	1	9	3	2	3
4	8	2	5	1	2
2	1	8	7	8	1
1	6	6	9	0	0
6	5	4	6	6	9

Puzzle A

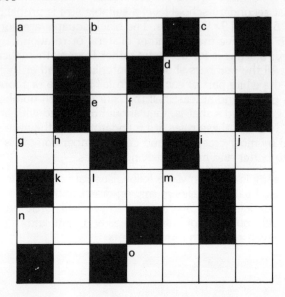

Clues across
a 1844 + 1613
d three-eighths of 1000
e 2586 + 4266
g 714 ÷ 34
i 3^4
k 389 × 9
n 6!
o 4102 — 1457

Clues down
a 5041 — 1139
b four gross
c three times (**b** down)
d one-twentieth of 700
f 4 × 5 × 6 × 7
h 443 × 3
j (**d** down)²
l $\sqrt{2500}$
m the square of 14

Puzzle B

a		b	c		d
	e			f	
g			h		
i	j		k		l
	m	n			
o			p		

Clues across
a a perfect square
c a factor of (**e** across)
e the next leap year after
    (**b** down)
g a quarter of (**b** down)
h a power of 2
i an even number
k a multiple of 11
m ten times (**p** across)
o a multiple of (**i** across)
p an odd number

Clues down
a twice (**g** across)
b double (**a** down)
c a multiple of (**f** down)
d twice (**i** down)
f an odd number
h a multiple of (**e** across)
i a cube
j a factor of (**h** across)
l half of (**i** across)
n a multiple of (**j** down)

Codes and Ciphers

Age range   9 upwards

Mathematics   Operations and functions

Equipment   Pencil and paper

Method of play

A code is a way of writing a message so as to conceal its true meaning. Most of the codes which are suitable for use in this game are actually ciphers – that is, they operate on individual letters rather than on complete words. Depending on pupils' ability and experience, the game may be played in several different ways.

1 A pupil is given the 'key' to a code – that is, a set of instructions for encoding and decoding messages – and is then asked to encode a given message and/or to decode another.

2 A pupil is asked to invent a code or cipher and to use this to encode a message of his/her own choice, giving it to a friend to decode.

3 A pupil is given a message written in an unknown code and is asked to 'break' the code and interpret the message. A hint of some sort, either to the nature of the code or to the contents of the message, will almost certainly be needed unless the message is long enough for the application of 'letter frequency' methods.

Notes

There are many different codes and ciphers available, and examples are to be found in a number of children's and other books. Among ciphers there are, broadly, three methods of working.

1 LETTER SUBSTITUTION   in which each letter is replaced according to an agreed rule. For example, each letter might be replaced by (a) its numerical position in the alphabet, or (b) its immediate successor, or (c) a sequence of dots and dashes, as in Morse code, or (d) a recognisable design, as in semaphore or Sherlock Holmes' 'dancing men'.

2 LETTER REARRANGEMENT where the letters are unchanged but are written in a different order. They may be split into groups of five and each group reversed, for instance; or the message may be written in a rectangle by rows and read off by columns.

3 LETTER CONCEALMENT in which the letters of the message are hidden (according to certain rules) within a longer meaningless message. Perhaps every third letter is genuine, or the last letter of each word, or the letter immediately following every capital.

To make the code more difficult to break, two or more of these methods may be combined; for example, the letters may be substituted *and* reversed.

Some interesting letter substitutions are those which deal with two or more letters simultaneously – these are much more difficult to decode without the key. One such method replaces each letter by its numerical value, converts each pair of numbers into a column vector, and then pre-multiplies by a given matrix to obtain another column vector which can be converted into two more letters. Decoding involves multiplication by the inverse matrix. Another bigram substitution is the well-known Playfair cipher, which is described in several books on codes.

Examples

The following cipher messages may be 'breakable' by fairly able pupils.

1 A cipher of a very familiar type: ZIOL EOHITK, GY EGXKLT, OL Q LODHST STZZTK LXWLZOZXZOGF WQLTR GF ZIT QKKQFUTDTFZ GY STZZTKL GF Q LZQFRQKR ZNHTVKOZTK ATNWGQKR.

2 6-75-85-53-8-102-9-90-53-16-6-53-15-1-68-74-33-102-52-33-39-33-53-22-50-8-52-23-68-39-15-1-88-34-90-85-20-7-4-94-22-7-6-53-15-1-68-39-8-92-9-53-60-90-85-16-92-6-2-33-39-15-1-88-34-16-33-ELEMENTARY CODE-20-7-20-92-34-75-13-50-47-16. (A Chemistry textbook might be helpful.)

3 SIHTX VASIC SYREQ LPMIA PICEH TREHF LOSOP
NOEVS OYECL AERUR ESILO TAHTW LEHTG LTSAD
ETTEB EFORS GHCAZ PUORA DASIT YMMUE.

Answers

1 This cipher is a simple letter substitution based on the
arrangement of letters on a standard typewriter keyboard.

2 Creation of this cipher was not easy as it is not every phrase
that can be put in cipher. You find that such easy phrases as
'elementary code' can cause real snags. (The atomic numbers
of elements are replaced by their symbols, ignoring capitals.)

3 This is a very simple cipher to solve once you realise that the
last letter of each group is a dummy.

Queens

Age range 11 to 14

Mathematics Problem-solving; spatial skills

Equipment A chessboard and eight queens (or other pieces)

Method of play

In chess, a queen can move any distance in a horizontal, vertical
or diagonal line. The object of the game is to place the eight
queens on the board so that none of them attacks any other.
(That is, no two must be in the same horizontal, vertical or
diagonal line.)

Solution

One possible solution is shown in the diagram below.

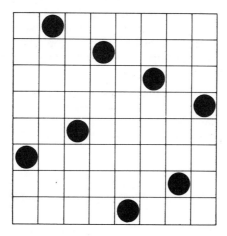

Note

This game can also be played by marking crosses in an 8 × 8 grid
on a piece of paper.

Four Fours

Age range   10 upwards

Mathematics   Problem-solving; arithmetic skills; operations

Equipment   Pencil and paper

Method of play

The object of the game is to use exactly four 4s, with any mathematical symbols that may be required, but no other figures, to make each of the whole numbers in turn.

Notes

Quite a lot of numbers can be constructed using just +, -, × and ÷ as operations, but some gaps remain. With the addition of √ (since √4=2) and ! (where 4!=24) every number up to 30 can be formed without too much difficulty. To go further will probably involve the use of both ·4 and ·$\dot{4}$ (which must be written *without* a 0 in the units place, contrary to the best mathematical practice), and even 4% is helpful on occasion. Using these symbols, every number up to 100 can be constructed in at least one way, as the solutions show.

Similar (but less well-known) games require pupils to construct numbers using 1, 2, 3 and 4 (in any order), or 1, 3, 5 and 7. A further rather difficult exercise uses the digits of the current year, and some variations even insist that these should be used in the correct order.

Solutions
The following solutions are not unique – they are not even necessarily the 'best' solutions.

$1 = 44 \div 44$

$2 = (4 \times 4) \div (4 + 4)$

$3 = (4 + 4 + 4) \div 4$

$4 = 4 + 4 - \sqrt{4} - \sqrt{4}$

$5 = \sqrt{4} + \sqrt{4} + (4 \div 4)$

$6 = 4 + 4 - 4 + \sqrt{4}$

$7 = 4 + 4 - (4 \div 4)$

$8 = 4 + 4 + 4 - 4$

$9 = 4 + 4 + (4 \div 4)$

$10 = 44 \div 4 \cdot 4$

$11 = 44 \div (\sqrt{4} \times \sqrt{4})$

$12 = (44 + 4) \div 4$

$13 = (44 \div 4) + \sqrt{4}$

$14 = 4 + 4 + 4 + \sqrt{4}$

$15 = (44 \div 4) + 4$

$16 = 4 + 4 + 4 + 4$

$17 = 4 \times 4 + (4 \div 4)$

$18 = 4 \times 4 + 4 - \sqrt{4}$

$19 = 4! - 4 - (4 \div 4)$

$20 = 4 \times 4 + \sqrt{4} + \sqrt{4}$

$21 = 4! - 4 - (4 \div 4)$

$22 = (44 \div 4) \times \sqrt{4}$

$23 = 4! - \sqrt{4} + (4 \div 4)$

$24 = (4 \times 4) + 4 + 4$

$25 = 4! + \sqrt{4} - (4 \div 4)$

$26 = 4! + ((4 + 4) \div 4)$

$27 = 4! + 4 - (4 \div 4)$

$28 = 4! + 4 + 4 - 4$

$29 = 4! + 4 + (4 \div 4)$

$30 = 4! + \sqrt{4} + \sqrt{4} + \sqrt{4}$

$31 = 4! + \sqrt{4} + (\sqrt{4} \div \cdot 4)$

$32 = (4 \times 4) + (4 \times 4)$

$33 = 4! + 4 + (\sqrt{4} \div \cdot 4)$

$34 = 4! + 4 + 4 + \sqrt{4}$

$35 = 4! + (44 \div 4)$

$36 = 44 - 4 - 4$

$37 = 4! + 4 + (4 \div \cdot \dot{4})$

$38 = 44 - 4 - \sqrt{4}$

$39 = 44 - (\sqrt{4} \div \cdot 4)$

$40 = 44 - \sqrt{4} - \sqrt{4}$

$41 = (\sqrt{4} \div 4\%) - (4 \div \cdot \dot{4})$

$42 = 44 - 4 + \sqrt{4}$

$43 = 44 - (4 \div 4)$

$44 = 44 - 4 + 4$

$45 = 44 + (4 \div 4)$

$46 = 44 + 4 - \sqrt{4}$

$47 = 4! + 4! - (4 \div 4)$

$48 = 44 + \sqrt{4} + \sqrt{4}$

$49 = 4! + 4! + (4 \div 4)$

$50 = 44 + 4 + \sqrt{4}$

$51 = (4! - 4 + \cdot 4) \div \cdot 4$

$52 = 44 + 4 + 4$

$53 = (4! \div \cdot \dot{4}) - (4 \div 4)$

$54 = 4! + 4! + 4 + \sqrt{4}$

$55 = (4! \div \cdot \dot{4}) + (4 \div 4)$

$56 = 4! + 4! + 4 + 4$

$57 = (4! - \cdot 4) \div \cdot 4 - \sqrt{4}$

$58 = (4! \div \cdot 4) - (4 \div \sqrt{4})$

$59 = (4! \div \cdot 4) - (4 \div 4)$

$60 = (4 \times 4 \times 4) - 4$

$61 = (4! \div \cdot 4) + (4 \div 4)$

$62 = (4 \times 4 \times 4) - \sqrt{4}$

$63 = (4! + \cdot 4) \div \cdot 4 + \sqrt{4}$

$64 = 4 \times 4 \times \sqrt{4} \times \sqrt{4}$

$65 = (4! + \cdot 4) \div \cdot 4 + 4$

$66 = (4 \times 4 \times 4) + \sqrt{4}$

$67 = (4! + \sqrt{4}) \div \cdot 4 + \sqrt{4}$

$68 = (4 \times 4 \times 4) + 4$

$69 = (4! + 4 - \cdot 4) \div \cdot 4$

$70 = (4! + \sqrt{4} + \sqrt{4}) \div \cdot 4$

$71 = (4! + 4 \cdot 4) \div \cdot 4$

$72 = (4 + 4) \times (4 \div \dot{4})$

$73 = \sqrt{4} \div \cdot \dot{4} + 4\% - \sqrt{4}$

$74 = (4! + 4) \div \cdot 4 + 4$

$75 = (4! + 4 + \sqrt{4}) \div \cdot 4$

$76 = (4! - 4) \times 4 - 4$

$77 = (4! - \cdot \dot{4}) \div \cdot \dot{4} + 4!$

$78 = (4! - 4) \times 4 - \sqrt{4}$

$79 = (4! + \cdot \dot{4}) \div \cdot \dot{4} + 4!$

$80 = (4 + 4) \times (4 \div \cdot 4)$

$81 = (4 \times 4) \div (\cdot \dot{4} \times \cdot \dot{4})$

$82 = (4! - 4) \times 4 + 4$

$83 = (4! - \cdot 4) \div \cdot 4 + 4!$

$84 = (4! - 4) \times 4 + 4$

$85 = (4! + \cdot 4) \div \cdot 4 + 4!$

$86 = 44 \times \sqrt{4} - \sqrt{4}$

$87 = (4! + 4) \div \cdot 4 + 4!$

$88 = (4! - 4) \times 4 \cdot 4$

$89 = (4! + \sqrt{4}) \div \cdot 4 + 4!$

$90 = 44 \times \sqrt{4} + \sqrt{4}$

$91 = 4! \times 4 - (\sqrt{4} \div \cdot 4)$

$92 = 44 \times \sqrt{4} + 4$

$93 = 4! \times 4 - \sqrt{4} \div \cdot \dot{4}$

$94 = (4! + 4) \div \cdot 4 + 4!$

$95 = 4! \times 4 - (4 \div 4)$

$96 = 4! + 4! + 4! + 4!$

$97 = (44 \div \cdot \dot{4}) - \sqrt{4}$

$98 = 4! \times 4 + (4 \div \sqrt{4})$

$99 = (4 \div 4\%) - (4 \div 4)$

$100 = 44 \div 44\%$

Magic Squares

Age range   11 to 16

Mathematics   Problem-solving; basic arithmetic

Equipment   Pencil and paper

Method of play

A magic square is an arrangement of numbers (all different) in a solid square such that each row, each column, and each main diagonal has the same total. Pupils are asked to construct their own magic squares using the whole numbers from 1 to 9 once each. The task is simply stated, but it is by no means trivial and will demand some patience (and perhaps a little luck) for successful completion.

Hints

Depending on the pupils' ability, teachers may wish to give any or all of the following hints, either at the start or during the period of solution.

1 Many pupils find it helpful to write the individual numbers on small pieces of paper and move them around physically while they search for possible solutions.

2 Since the nine numbers add up to 45, the 'magic total' of each row, column and diagonal must be 15.

3 A pupil who has trouble even starting might try the middle number (that is, 5) in the middle square.

Notes

The 3 × 3 magic square shown opposite is a unique solution, except for the obvious reflections and rotations. However, further magic squares can be obtained by linear transformations of its elements (e.g. doubling each number, or adding 4, or both).

An able fifth-year pupil might be asked to construct a magic square using only prime numbers; this is considerably more difficult than the first task, as can be seen from the size of the numbers in the solution shown.

Not many pupils will be able to construct a 4×4 magic square (using numbers 1 to 16) without a good deal of help. However, the square shown in the solution below is not only magic but 'diabolical', with many more groups of numbers totalling 34 than immediately apparent. Any pupil given a duplicated sheet with (say) fifty copies of this square should have no difficulty in finding thirty or forty sets of four numbers (mostly in recognisable patterns) which add up to 34.

Solutions

2	9	4
7	5	3
6	1	8

A 3×3 magic square

41	113	59
89	71	53
83	29	101

A prime magic square

5	10	3	16
4	15	6	9
14	1	12	7
11	8	13	2

A 4×4 'diabolical' square

Pentominoes

Age range   11 upwards

Mathematics   Spatial relationships

Equipment   A set of pentominoes

Method of play

Each pupil is supplied with a set of pentominoes, either ready-made or drawn on paper ready for cutting out, and has to assemble them to make a rectangle.

Preparation

Just as a domino consists of two adjacent squares, so a pentomino is made of five squares joined along their edges. A complete set, representing all the possible shapes (apart from reflections) consists of twelve pentominoes, as shown below.

These are best made of plywood, hardboard or plastic, but a set for one use only can easily be duplicated (for cutting out) onto card or paper. Each square should have an edge of about 2 cm for ease of handling.

Solutions

Rectangles measuring 10×6 squares, 12×5, 15×4 and 20×3 can all be constructed, as the diagrams below show, although these are by no means the only possible solutions.

Variation

A set of pentominoes can be used for a two-player game, together with a 8×8 board (e.g. a chessboard) with squares the same size as those of the pentominoes. Each player in turn takes one of the pentominoes and places it on the board so as to cover five squares exactly; the first player who is unable to play in his or her turn loses.

As Others See Us

Age range   12 to 16

Mathematics   Spatial skills; drawing skills

Equipment   Pencil and paper; various books, boxes, etc.

Method of play

Three or four objects are arranged in a three-dimensional group on a table; initially, it is a good idea to keep the arrangement quite simple. Each pupil is seated at one side of this table, and has to sketch the arrangement *as it would look from the other side*, without leaving his or her seat.

Cryptarithmetics

Age range   12 upwards

Mathematics   Problem solving; arithmetic skills

Equipment   Prepared puzzles; pencil and paper

Method of play

Each pupil is given a number of worked calculations in which
some or all of the figures are missing. In some cases these figures
may be replaced by stars or spots, in other cases by letters, with
the same letter representing the same figure (and different letters
different figures) throughout the calculation. Each calculation is
properly set out, using the format customary in the school, but
leading zeroes, 'carrying' and 'borrowing' figures, and remainders
in short division, are not normally shown. The pupil's aim is to
discover the missing figures and so reconstruct the calculation.

Methods of solution

Although no two problems are exactly alike, some hints may be
found helpful. The number of figures in a number is often
important; if two three-figure numbers are added together to give
a four-figure number, for example, the first figure of the answer
must be 1. Similarly, if a multiplication shows that 8 times a two-
figure number still has two figures, then the number must be 10,
11 or 12. At the other extreme, if a three-figure number
subtracted from a four-figure number gives a two-figure answer,
the first two numbers must start with 9 and with 10 respectively.

Another useful technique is to look at last figures (especially of
multiplications); if a particular multiplication is known to end in 5,
for example, one of the factors must end in 5 and the other must
end in an odd number (perhaps 5 again).

With alphamatics (that is, puzzles which use letters rather than
stars) there are some further possibilities. If it appears, for
instance, that $A+B=A$, then $B=0$ is not the only possible solution
(except in the units column); it may be that $B=9$ and that there
has been a 'carry' from the column to the right. (It may even be,
in some cases, that $B=8$ or 7 and that there has been a 'carry' of
2 or 3.) Points such as these are discovered by experience, but

at the beginning many pupils will find cryptarithmetics very difficult and may need some guidance if they are not to become totally disheartened.

Variation

Once pupils have mastered the art of solving cryptarithmetics, they can begin to construct their own, aiming always to produce a puzzle that has a unique solution.

Examples

The following cryptarithmetics are ranged in approximate order of difficulty – the last few are hard enough to interest academic sixth-formers.

```
1    *  1  5           2    2  7  *
   +  2  *  3             -  1  *  3
   ─────────             ─────────
      5  5  *                *  2  0


3       4  6           4   4 ) *  5  2
     ×     *                      3  *
     ───────                  ─────────
     *  *  2


5       *  3           6   * ) 8  *  5
     ×     6                      *  *
     ───────                  ─────────
     2  *  *


7    *  0  *           8         *  *
   -  7  *  9              ×      7  *
   ─────────              ───────────
     *  8  6              *  *  *
                         *  *
                      ───────────
                      *  *  2  *
```

26

```
9      A B          10    A B C
  +    B A             —  C B A
      ─────               ─────
      C B C               C A B

11  A) A B C        12    A B C
       B D A             ×     A
       ─────               ─────
                          B C C

13     A B B        14    *  *  *
       A B              ×     8  *
  +    B B               ─────────
      ─────              *  *  *  *
      B B B              *  *  *
                         ─────────
                         *  *  *  *
                         ─────────

15              A C
     A B C ) B E F G
             D A B
             ─────
             H J G
             H J G
             ─────
```

Crazy Cubes

Age range   12 upwards

Mathematics   Modelling; problem-solving

Equipment   Nets of four cubes; glue, colours

Method of play

Each pupil should colour as instructed, then cut out and glue together, the nets of the four cubes shown below. (It may be advisable to make and duplicate a larger version of each net for ease of handling, but the colouring instructions should not be changed.) Once the cubes are assembled, the object of the game is to arrange them in a single pile four cubes high so that each side of the pile shows all four colours, once each.

Cube 1

	red	
green	blue	yellow
	green	
	yellow	

Cube 2

	yellow	
red	red	red
	blue	
	green	

Cube 3		
	red	
green	yellow	red
	blue	
	yellow	

Cube 4		
	blue	
yellow	red	green
	red	
	yellow	

Solution

One solution, with the cubes stacked in order from cube 1 at the top to cube 4 at the bottom, produces sides coloured as follows.

Y	G	B	Y
R	Y	G	B
B	R	R	G
G	B	Y	R

Note

Pupils may like to experiment with their own colour schemes, but should be warned that some colour schemes will make the solution very easy, while others make it impossible.

GAMES FOR TWO
PLAYERS

The games in this section are intended for two players, each
competing against the other on more or less equal terms. Most
of them, however, could be played equally well between two
teams each of two or three pupils, and the discussion this would
generate could be a valuable learning experience.

Fingers

Age range   9 to 11

Mathematics   Strategy; elementary probability

Equipment   None

Method of play

Players begin with their hands behind their backs. On an agreed signal (for example, 'One, two, three, go!') each of them displays one, two or three fingers, and *simultaneously* calls out his or her guess at the total number of fingers (from two to six) displayed. A player who guesses right scores one point. The game is then repeated as many times as the players wish.

Notes

There is no sure winning strategy, but players will soon realise that their own fingers restrict the possibilities. It should also become apparent that each player needs to vary his/her finger selections, since otherwise the opponent will easily be able to guess correctly.

Thirty-one

Age range   9 to 11

Mathematics   Strategy; mental arithmetic

Equipment   None

Method of play

Each player in turn names a number between one and five (inclusive). This number is added to a running total, and the winner is the player who takes the total to exactly 31.

Notes

There is a simple and fairly obvious winning strategy for this game, and pupils may be encouraged to look for it. If the first player begins by choosing 1, then no matter what numbers the second player may choose the first can always take the total up to 7, 13, 19, 25 and 31 on successive turns. On the other hand, any other choice by the first player will allow the second player to achieve this sequence.

Noughts and Crosses (1)

Age range   9 to 11

Mathematics   Strategy; spatial skills

Equipment   Paper and pencils

Method of play

The basic game is widely known, and is played on a grid of 3 × 3 squares as shown. The players alternately put a symbol in any vacant square – the first player normally uses a cross, and the second a nought – with the aim of making a line of three crosses or three noughts horizontally, vertically or diagonally. In the partially completed game below, the first player can thus win on the next turn.

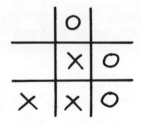

Notes

There is no winning strategy for this game, but most pupils are able to develop fairly quickly a non-losing strategy, and games thereafter will normally result in a draw. When that stage is reached, it is time to move onto one of the variations described in the following pages.

Noughts and Crosses (2)

Age range   11 to 16

Mathematics   Strategy; spatial skills

Equipment   Playing grid; three black and three white counters

Method of play

The game is played in two phases. In the first phase, each player alternately places a counter of his/her colour in any vacant square. Once all six counters are in place, however, each player continues by sliding one of his/her counters into an adjacent empty square, and the game continues in this way until one player achieves a line of three counters.

Noughts and Crosses (3)

Age range   11 upwards

Mathematics   Strategy; spatial skills

Equipment   Squared paper; pencils

Method of play

In this extension of basic *Noughts and Crosses* an infinite grid is used (although in practice 20 × 20 squares is almost always enough), and the players' aim is to get five noughts or five crosses in a line, rather than three.

Example

The diagram below shows a game in progress. 6 mm or 8 mm squared paper is ideal for this purpose.

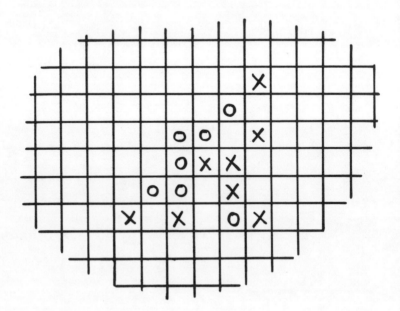

Noughts and Crosses (4)

Age range   14 upwards

Mathematics   Strategy; spatial skills in three dimensions

Equipment   Playing board; counters (but see variation below)

Method of play

The playing board consists of four grids of 4×4 squares,
arranged one above the other so as to give a playing area of
4×4×4 positions. On this board, the players play *Noughts and
Crosses* in three dimensions, each trying to form a line of four
counters of his/her colour in any direction.

Playing board

This is illustrated in the sketch below, and every effort should be
made to get a proper board either commercially or by
negotiation with the Craft and Technology Department. Ideally,
the shelves should be made of clear plastic so that all positions
are easily examined.

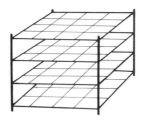

Variation

Able sixth-formers with considerable powers of imagination can
play this game using just pencils and paper. In this case the four
levels of the playing area are drawn as four square grids side by
side; it must be remembered that a 'line' in this situation might
consist of one cross in each grid.

Kayles

Age range   9 to 13

Mathematics   Strategy; spatial relationships

Equipment   About 20 matches or other tokens

Method of play

The tokens are laid out in a single row, touching one another.
Two players alternately take *either* a single token from
anywhere in the row, *or* two touching tokens (if any such
remain); the player who takes the last token (either alone or as
one of a touching pair) is the winner.

Notes

At the beginning of the game, few pupils will have any coherent
strategy, but the abler ones may be able to plan the last few
moves once the number of tokens decreases. For example, it is
clear that a player who leaves two isolated tokens at the end of
her turn is bound to win, while another who leaves two groups of
two is likely to lose if his opponent is alert. Once pupils are
familiar with the game, the teacher may wish to encourage such
strategic thinking.

Homeward Bound

Age range   9 to 13

Mathematics   Strategy; spatial relationships

Equipment   Grid (see below); pencils

Method of play

A playing grid of 10 × 10 dots is prepared as in the example
below, and a 'red home', a 'blue home', and a 'start' are marked
as shown. One player is 'red' and the other 'blue', and each in
turn adds a unit line segment (either horizontal or vertical) to the
end of an ever-growing chain, with the aim of taking the chain to
his/her own 'home'. The chain may not go outside the grid, nor
may it visit any point of the grid more than once. The winner is
the player at whose 'home' the chain eventually arrives;
alternatively, if one player has no legal move available in his/her
turn, the other is the winner.

Example

The diagram below shows a game in progress. Note that there is
no need for the players to use differently coloured pencils,
although they may do so if they wish.

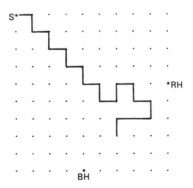

N.B.   A playing grid suitable for duplicating may be found on
page 116.

Battleships

Age range 9 to 13

Mathematics Strategy; logical reasoning; coordinates

Equipment Playing grids; pencils

Method of play

Each player has two grids (one for his/her own fleet, the other for recording the results of shooting), which are kept hidden from his/her opponent. On the first grid, each player marks the positions of four ships: a battleship occupying four adjacent squares in a horizontal or vertical line, a cruiser occupying three squares similarly, a destroyer in two squares, and a frigate needing only a single square.

Each player in turn fires a salvo of shots at the other's fleet, the point of each shot being identified by its coordinates. The number of shots in the salvo is equal to the number of undamaged squares of the player's own ships (and so initially ten, but decreasing as the battle proceeds). At the end of the salvo, the other player announces the result, saying (for example), 'All your shots missed', or 'You sank my frigate and scored one hit on my cruiser.' However, the opponent does *not* say which particular shots (if any) were the successful ones – the player must try to deduce that by other means.

The battle continues in this way until one player's fleet is entirely destroyed.

Notes

Many players find it helpful to keep a record of their shots in the form shown in the example opposite. The numbers in the grid indicate the number of the salvo, while the notes below show the hits (if any) and so allow for deductions to be made. For example, the cruiser has been hit in salvoes 1 and 3, so its third square can only be at c2, c6 or h3.

These coordinates, of course, identify squares rather than points as in Cartesian geometry. To avoid confusion, therefore, it may be advisable to play this game some time *before* formal Cartesian coordinates are introduced, rather than at the same time.

Example

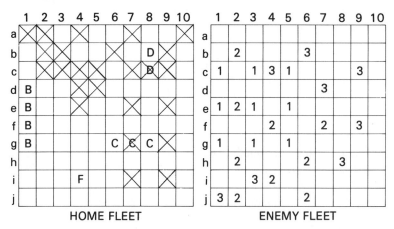

HOME FLEET   ENEMY FLEET

Salvo

1   1 hit cruiser
2   frigate sunk
3   1 hit cruiser
4
5

N.B.   A playing grid suitable for duplicating may be found on page 117.

Fifteen Up

Age range   9 to 13

Mathematics   Strategy; mental arithmetic

Equipment   Nine cards, numbered 1 to 9

Method of play

The nine cards are laid face up on the table, and each player in turn chooses and takes into his/her hand any one of the cards remaining. The winner is the first player who is able to lay down from his/her hand a set of *three* cards totalling 15.

Notes

Only the most able pupils are likely to realise that this game is isomorphic to *Noughts and Crosses*, via magic squares. However, this fact means

(a) that some 'blocking' play may be needed, where a card is chosen because of its value to one's opponent rather than to oneself, and

(b) that a game may well end in a draw, with neither player able to make 15.

Poison

Age range   9 to 13

Mathematics   Strategy; rectangles

Equipment   Playing grid (see below); pencils

Method of play

On a grid of 10 × 10 squares, one player chooses a single square and marks it with a cross, denoting a bottle of poison. The two players in turn then choose and shade a rectangle anywhere on the grid; the sides of the rectangle must be whole numbers of squares, and the rectangle must not cross any area that has already been shaded. The player who is forced to shade the square containing the poison loses the game.

Notes

The term 'rectangle' naturally includes squares even as small as 1 × 1. The diagram below shows a game in progress.

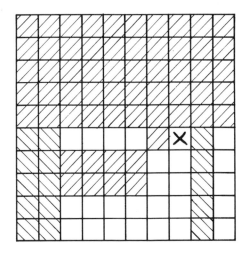

N.B.   A playing grid suitable for duplicating may be found on page 117.

Odd and Even

Age range   9 to 13

Mathematics   Strategy; number skills

Equipment   15 tokens (matches or counters)

Method of play

The fifteen tokens are placed in a pile on the table, and players
alternately take either one or two until the pile is exhausted.
The winner is the player who finishes with an odd number of
tokens.

Filling Squares

Age range   9 to 13

Mathematics   Strategy; areas

Equipment   Playing grid; coloured pencils

Method of play

On a grid of 10 × 10 dots, as below, each player in turn marks a unit line segment (horizontal or vertical) anywhere on the grid. Any player drawing the segment which completes a square (of any size) may claim the whole area within that square, except any that has already been claimed as part of another square, and shade it in his/her colour. No further lines may then be drawn within the shaded area. When the entire grid has been shaded, the player who has claimed the greater *area* (not necessarily the greater number of squares) is the winner.

Example

The grid below shows a game in progress.

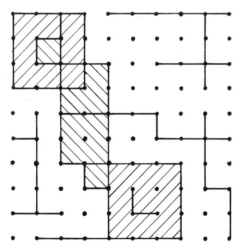

N.B.   A playing grid suitable for duplicating may be found on page 116.

Think of a Number

Age range   9 to 14

Mathematics   Mental arithmetic; elementary algebra

Equipment   None

Method of play

The 'inventor' gives the 'calculator' a set of simple instructions such as the following:

> think of a number
> double it
> add four
> multiply by five
> add twenty
> divide by ten
> take away the number you first thought of
> . . . and your answer is four.

The game should be introduced by the teacher, after which pupils should be invited to invent their own sets of instructions – each leading to the same answer no matter what number is originally chosen – and try them out on one another.

Variation

In a variation of this game, the inventor does not announce the answer, but instead asks for the calculator's answer and immediately says, 'The number you thought of was . . .' This game is only a little more difficult, and is a natural extension of the game above.

Pathways

Age range   11 to 14

Mathematics   Strategy; spatial relationships

Equipment   Playing grids; pencils

Method of play

On a playing grid similar to that shown below, each player in turn marks a unit line segment between two symbols. One player uses only dots, with the aim of completing a continuous path between the two sides of the board; the other uses only crosses and tries to complete a path between top and bottom. Line segments may not cross one another, and the game ends when one player succeeds in completing a path.

Example

The diagram below shows a game in progress.

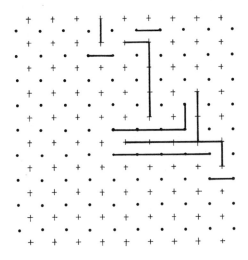

N.B. A playing grid suitable for duplicating may be found on page 118.

Bulls and Cows

Age range   11 upwards

Mathematics   Strategy; logical reasoning

Equipment   Pencil and paper

Method of play

One player is the 'setter' and the other the 'guesser'. The setter chooses (secretly) a four-digit number with all its digits different, and writes it down on a slip of paper to avoid any lapses of memory. The guesser then tries to discover this number. He/she writes down a four-digit number, to which the setter replies by announcing the number of 'bulls' (correct digits in the correct positions) and the number of 'cows' (correct digits in wrong positions). Only the total of each is announced, however, and the guesser is not told *which* are the correct digits. For example, if the secret number is 1483 and the guess 2381, the setter gives the reply, 'one bull and two cows'.

The guesser then writes down another guess, to which the setter again replies, and so on until the guesser discovers the whole number or admits defeat. The setter and guesser then change places, and the winner is the one who found the secret number in the smaller number of guesses (no matter whether the guesses were right or wrong).

Notes

This game is the traditional version of the game marketed commercially as *Mastermind*. It can be made considerably more difficult by abandoning the rule that all four digits must be different, and such a variation calls for a fair degree of skill and logical reasoning, unlikely to be found below the sixth form.

Hex

Age range 12 upwards

Mathematics Strategy; spatial relationships

Equipment Playing grid and pencils

Method of play

The game is played on a grid of interlocking hexagons. Each player in turn claims a hexagon by placing his/her symbol (usually a nought or a cross) in it; one player is trying to complete a chain of hexagons between the two black (or **X**) sides of the grid, while the other is trying to make a chain between the two white (or **O**) sides. The game ends when one of them succeeds.

Example

The diagram below shows part of the grid with a game in progress.

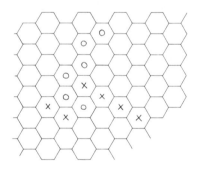

Notes

The game can also be played by placing counters (black or white) on the hexagons of a more permanent board. In concept it is very similar to *Pathways* already described.

N.B. A playing grid suitable for duplicating may be found on page 119.

Nim

Age range   12 upwards

Mathematics   Strategy; binary numbers

Equipment   About thirty tokens (e.g. matches)

Method of play

The tokens are placed on the table in three piles, not necessarily equal in size. Each player in turn can then take as many tokens as he/she wishes from any one pile – the minimum is one, the maximum is the whole pile. The player who succeeds in taking the last token (either alone or as one of the last pile) is the winner.

Strategy

After playing this game a few times, most pupils can develop a logical strategy to cope with the last few moves. However, there is a clear strategy for the whole game, based on the use of binary numbers, and after the pupils know and understand the game teachers may wish to introduce this strategy. A player who hopes to win should aim always to leave the table in such a state that if the number of tokens in each pile is converted to a binary number, the total of each binary column is even. To see how this works, consider a sample game between Janet (who knows the strategy) and John (who does not).

Janet sets out three piles of tokens at random: 4   7   10
John takes 2 tokens from the middle pile: 4   5   10
Janet converts these numbers to binary form –

  4 =   1   0   0
  5 =   1   0   1
10 = 1   0   1   0

and sees that the first, third and fourth binary columns have odd totals. By reducing the third pile to 1, she can give all the columns even totals, so she takes 9 tokens from
the third pile: 4   5   1
John, playing without any strategy, takes 3 tokens from the
middle pile: 4   2   1

Janet does another mental conversion –

```
4 = 1   0   0
2 =     1   0
1 =         1
```

and decides to reduce the first pile to 3 (binary 11), so giving the three binary columns totals of 0, 2 and 2 respectively. Janet therefore takes one token from the first pile: 3 2 1
John takes two tokens from the first pile: 1 2 1
Janet now does her mental arithmetic again, and realises that two equal piles (and the third empty) will always give even totals. She takes all the middle pile away: 1 0 1
John sees at this point that he has lost. He takes one token: 0 0 1
and Janet takes the other and wins.

Notes

Once both players know the strategy and are proficient in its use, the result of the game depends entirely on the initial sizes of the piles. The game may be varied, however, by increasing the initial *number* of piles to four or five, or (quite commonly) by reversing the winning rule so that the aim is to force one's opponent to take the last token. Neither of these variations has any major effect on the early stages of the game, but the reversal rule does change the last few moves quite significantly.

Yahtzee

Age range   13 upwards

Mathematics   Probability

Equipment   Five dice; pencil and paper

Method of play

Each player in turn throws the five dice together. If the player is not satisfied with the result, he/she may throw any or all of the dice a second time, leaving the rest as they fell; similarly, a third throw of any or all of the dice is allowed if the player so wishes. The combination of dice after the third throw (or when the player chooses to stop, if earlier) is what will be scored.

The score card and scoring rules are shown opposite, and the player may choose to score a combination in any empty box. For example, the combination 3-3-3-5-6 could be scored as 'threes' (scoring 9), or as 'three of a kind' (scoring 20), or as 'fives' (scoring 5 only), or as 'full house' (scoring 0, since it does not actually qualify), or in any other way. Once the choice is made, however, it cannot be changed, and no subsequent throw can be scored in that same box. (The one exception is 'Yahtzee' – a genuine Yahtzee can be scored as many times as it is thrown.) When both players have filled all thirteen scoring boxes (and if one player has scored Yahtzee more than once, some extra throws may be needed to achieve this) the one with the higher total score is the winner.

Scoring

The score card has thirteen boxes, as shown.

Ones		Three of a kind	
Twos		Full house	
Threes		Four of a kind	
Fours		Low straight	
Fives		High straight	
Sixes		Chance	
Yahtzee			

In these boxes, the method of scoring is as follows.
Ones scores the total of the dice showing 1 (for example,
1-1-1-3-4 scores 3).
Twos scores the total of the dice showing 2 (for example,
1-2-2-3-5 scores 4).
Threes, Fours, Fives and *Sixes* score similarly.
Three of a kind scores the total of all five dice provided that at
least three of them are showing the same number, otherwise
nothing.
Full house scores the total of all five dice provided that three of
them show one number and the other two show another number
(for example, 2-2-5-5-5).
Four of a kind scores the total of all five dice provided that four
of them are showing the same number.
Low straight scores 30 if four of the dice form a sequence of
consecutive numbers (i.e. 1-2-3-4 or 2-3-4-5 or 3-4-5-6), otherwise
nothing.
High straight scores 40 if all five dice form a sequence of
consecutive numbers (1-2-3-4-5 or 2-3-4-5-6), otherwise nothing.
Chance scores the total of all five dice, whatever they are.
(Like the other boxes above, however, this score can be claimed
only once.)
Yahtzee scores 50 if all five dice show the same number,
otherwise nothing. Unlike any other score, this can be claimed
more than once in a game if a second Yahtzee is thrown.

Notes

Intuitive (if not formal) ideas of probability are needed at two
stages in this game – first in deciding how many dice (if any) to
throw again, and second in deciding where to enter a score. For
example, if after the first throw the dice show 1-2-2-4-5, is it
better to throw one die in the hope of obtaining a high straight,
or three with the intention of scoring the result in the 'twos'
box? And then, if the end result is 2-2-2-3-5, should it be scored
as 'twos' (worth 6) or 'three of a kind' (worth 14, but possibly
shutting out a better score later)? Teachers may wish to develop
either or both of these points through formal teaching.

Sprouts

Age range   13 upwards

Mathematics   Strategy; basic topology

Equipment   Pencil and paper

Method of play

A few dots (about four or five) are clearly marked on a sheet of paper. Each player in turn then joins any two dots with an arc, and marks a new dot on this arc. There are just two restrictions: no dot may have more than three arcs emerging from it, and no two arcs may cross one another. The first player who is unable to make a legal move loses the game.

Notes

Players must understand the principle on which arcs are counted. If two dots A and B are joined by an arc and a new dot C marked on the arc as in the diagram, then A and B now each have one arc emerging from them but C has two arcs (one joining it to A, the other to B) and so is allowed only one more. It is important to note, too, that 'arc' is used in a topological rather than a geometrical sense, and that the line can be any shape (not necessarily part of a circle).

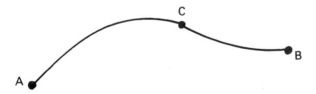

Owari

Age range   14 upwards

Mathematics   Strategy; mental arithmetic

Equipment   12 small cups; 48 dried peas or similar

Method of play

The cups are set out in two rows of six, between the two
players, and four peas are placed in each cup. Each player in
turn then takes all the peas out of any one cup in the row nearer
to him/her, and drops them (one per cup) into the next few
cups, moving round in a clockwise direction. For example, if the
situation before Bob's turn is:

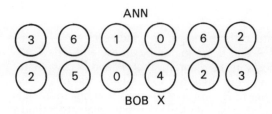

and Bob decides to empty cup X, the situation after his turn will
be this.

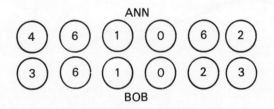

(If the cup emptied contains 12 or more peas, then more than
one circuit will be needed; in this case, the cup just emptied is
left out when the peas are dropped.)

If the last pea is dropped into a cup on the opponent's side, and makes the total number of peas in that cup either two or three, the player may capture those peas and remove them from the game. Similarly, if the last-but-one pea fell into an opponent's cup and made the total two or three, those peas too may be captured provided that the last pea gave a capture; and if two cups have been captured then the last-but-two is also vulnerable, and so on. However, only adjacent cups (starting from the last pea) on the opponent's side are vulnerable in this way.

For example, if we continue with the game above, it is now Ann's turn, and she may choose to empty the second cup from the left (as we look at it). This gives the position:

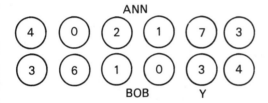

and Ann now captures the peas in the cup marked Y, and removes them.

The game ends when one or other player is unable to move, and the winner is the player who has captured the larger number of peas. (Of course, if one player captures more than 24 peas, he/she is certain to win and the game may be abandoned at that stage.)

Notes

Unlike most of the games in this book, this game (which has been played in West Africa for many years) takes quite a long time to complete, and at least half an hour (preferably more) should be allowed.

GAMES FOR SMALL GROUPS

The games in this section are intended to be played by groups of between four and six pupils, either as single groups or as subdivisions of the whole class.

Another Way

Age range   9 to 11

Mathematics   As required

Equipment   None

Method of play

One player, chosen at random, makes a mathematical statement (for example, 'six plus eight equals fourteen'). Each of the other players in turn then expresses the same fact in a different way (for instance, 'fourteen minus six equals eight', 'six is eight less than fourteen' and so on). When all have responded correctly, the round ends and another player makes the initial statement.

Notes

When the game is first played, it is a good idea for the teacher to make the initial statement and to remain in the group for a short while to assess the responses. Later, however, the group themselves can decide whether a particular response is acceptable, and can benefit from the discussion that this may engender.

Guess My Number

Age range   9 to 13

Mathematics   Strategy; number ordering

Equipment   None

Method of play

One player chooses (secretly) a whole number within a certain
range determined beforehand by the teacher, and the others try
to discover this number. Each of the other players in turn asks a
single question of the 'yes/no' type, and the questioning
continues until either the number is found or until the number of
questions asked reaches a limit set by the teacher.

Strategy

Most pupils discover fairly quickly that the most efficient
questioning strategy is one based on inequalities and interval
bisection. For example, if the chosen number is known to lie in
the range 1 to 100, the questioning might run as follows.

Is the number greater than 50?   Yes.
Is it greater than 75?   No.
Is it greater than 62?   Yes . . . and so on.

Notes

The game can be varied by the teacher's varying the range in
which the number may be chosen. To connect with a particular
topic, however, the choice could be extended to include common
and/or decimal fractions, or restricted to (say) prime numbers or
multiples of 6, with a corresponding adjustment in the number of
questions allowed.

Subtraction

Age range   9 to 13

Mathematics   Subtraction; basic probability

Equipment   Pencil and paper

Method of play

Each pupil prepares the outline of a subtraction in which a two-digit number is subtracted from a three-digit number, as shown in the diagram below.

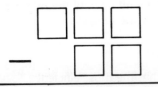

Five digits are then generated randomly (e.g. by throwing a ten-faced die or by using a table of random numbers) and as each digit is announced, each pupil writes it into one of the squares of his/her outline. Each digit must be written in before the next is announced, and once written it cannot be changed. When all five digits have been announced and written into place, each pupil carries out his or her subtraction, and the one with the largest result wins the round.

Variation

A similar game can be played using either addition or multiplication instead of subtraction; in the latter case, a calculator may be used for determining the final result.

Fraction Snap

Age range   9 to 13

Mathematics   Equivalent fractions

Equipment   Playing cards, prepared as described below

Method of play

The cards are dealt out, and pupils play an ordinary game of *Snap* using whatever rules may be desired. Two cards are considered to be equal in value (and hence 'snappable') if they show equivalent fractions. The game ends when one player has won all the cards, or after an agreed time when the player with most cards is declared the winner.

Preparation

An ordinary pack of playing cards may be used for a base, but each should be altered to show a fraction instead of a suit and a value. The fractions may be all common fractions, or (if the teacher so wishes) they may show decimals and/or percentages too. The fractions need not all be in their lowest terms, and each equivalent value should appear at least four times. As a guide, it is suggested that there might be eight cards with fractions equivalent to $\frac{1}{2}$ (including $\frac{1}{2}$ itself) and four each equivalent to $\frac{1}{3}$, $\frac{2}{3}$, $\frac{1}{4}$, $\frac{3}{4}$, $\frac{1}{5}$, $\frac{3}{5}$, $\frac{1}{8}$, $\frac{5}{8}$, $\frac{1}{10}$, $\frac{3}{10}$ and $\frac{7}{10}$, but teachers may clearly vary this as they think desirable.

Threes and Fives

Age range   9 to 13

Mathematics   Multiples

Equipment   A set of dominoes

Method of play

The dominoes are shared out among the players, and each player in turn then adds a domino to either end of a steadily lengthening chain. The first player can begin with any domino – it need not be the double-six – but thereafter touching ends must always show the same number. Doubles may be laid either along or across the chain, as the player wishes, but they do not create any new ends. A player must play a domino if possible, but otherwise misses a turn.

A player scores points if at the end of his/her turn the two ends of the chain total a multiple of three or of five. A total of three or five scores 1 point, of six or ten, 2 points, of nine, 3 points, of twelve or twenty, 4 points, and of eighteen, 6 points. A total of fifteen scores 8 points (5 for 5 threes, and 3 for 3 fives); a total of zero is also a multiple, of course, but scores nothing. Several hands are normally played, the winner being the first player to reach 31 points.

Example

The following moves in a game between Matthew, Mark, Luke and John illustrate the scoring process.

Matthew plays first. The ends total nine, so he scores 3 points.

Mark plays a double; the ends now total twelve (both halves of the double being counted), so Mark scores 4 points.

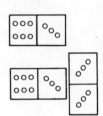

Luke plays the 6-4, and the total of the ends is now ten, so Luke scores 2 points.

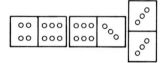

John plays the 4-1 and scores nothing, since 7 is not a multiple of 5 or 3.

Variations

Some variations of this game relate to the play of the dominoes themselves; for example, a player may be allowed to start a third or fourth 'end' from a double played across the chain, or players may start with only a few dominoes and draw from the 'boneyard' whenever they cannot play. Other variations require the player to claim points *before* laying down the domino being played, and/or allow other players to claim the points if the original player does not do so quickly enough.

Sum and Product

Age range   9 to 13

Mathematics   Mental arithmetic; algebraic factorisation

Equipment   None

Method of play

One player chooses (secretly) three whole numbers within a
certain range (say, 1 to 20) and states their sum and their
product. The other players then try to guess these numbers.
Each player in turn may guess at one, two or three of the
numbers, and the answer is either 'right' or 'wrong'. (If two or
three numbers are guessed, the answer is 'wrong' unless both or
all of them are correct.) The game ends when one player guesses
all three correctly.

Variations

Two variations can be used, according to the pupils' ages.

1 FOR YOUNGER PUPILS   The sum of all three numbers is stated
   as above, but the product *only of the first two* is given. (This
   keeps the product down to a manageable size.) It may well be
   desirable to restrict the range of the numbers too.
2 FOR OLDER PUPILS   The range of choice may be extended to
   take in negative numbers – care is clearly needed then in
   calculating the sum and the product. At some stage, a further
   variation might be to limit the choice to two (rather than three)
   numbers, so leading into the techniques involved in factorising
   trinomial expressions.

One Different

Age range   9 to 13

Mathematics   Logical reasoning

Equipment   Logic blocks (see below)

Method of play

The blocks are shared out so that each pupil has a small pile of them. Each in turn then plays one block into the centre of the table, which differs in exactly one attribute from the last block previously played. A pupil who is unable to play a block according to this rule must instead take any one block (except the last one) from the centre. The first player to get rid of all of his/her blocks is the winner.

Logic blocks

These are available from several educational suppliers (in complete sets) or can be made in school. Each block is normally considered to have four attributes:

shape   (triangular, square, hexagonal or circular)
colour   (red, yellow, green or blue)
size   (large or small)
thickness   (thick or thin)

and a full set thus contains 64 blocks, one with each possible combination of attributes. (Teachers making their own blocks, or negotiating with the Craft and Technology Department, can of course vary the shape and colour specifications if they so wish.)

Variation

A variation for older pupils involves giving them the whole set of blocks and asking them to lay out the blocks in a square or rectangular array so that each block differs in exactly one attribute from those horizontally and vertically adjacent to it.

Newspapers (1)

Age range   9 to 13

Mathematics   As required

Equipment   Old newspapers

Method of play

The group is given a newspaper and shares the pages among
pupils in any convenient way. Group members are then asked to
find items with a particular mathematical content (e.g. graphs,
percentages, or as determined by the teacher) and to cut these
out and make a wall display.

Notes

As an alternative, the group may simply be asked to find *any*
mathematical content in the newspaper and to identify it by
suitable labelling in the display. (The *Financial Times* is best
avoided for this game, unless the room has a *very* large notice
board!)

Newspapers (2)

Age range   9 to 16

Mathematics   As required

Equipment   Old newspapers; prepared questions

Method of play

The group is given a newspaper; if more than one group is
playing simultaneously, each group should have the same
newspaper. The teacher then asks a number of questions (with
such mathematical content as he/she wishes) which can be
answered by finding the information and possibly doing a simple
calculation; each group works as a team.

Notes

It is best if the questions are given all together in written form, so
that all pupils are able to share in the work. Suitable questions,
based on a particular issue, might be:

1 How long is it, in hours and minutes, between High Tide and
  Low Tide at London Bridge?.
2 How many French francs could I get for £100?
3 If 1100 people were asked, how many of them said that the
  nuclear power station should be closed down? (The paper
  reported '72 per cent'.)
4 If Everton wins its last eight matches this season, how many
  points will it finish with?
5 What percentage of the complaints of cruelty to animals last
  year led to convictions?

. . . and so on. Any national or local paper will give ample scope
for twenty questions or so.

Estimation Golf

Age range   9 upwards

Mathematics   Estimation and measurement

Equipment   Measuring instruments; prepared lengths etc. if desired

Method of play

The teacher announces a 'course' of eighteen 'holes', each hole being a distance, length, angle, weight or other quantity to be estimated. (These may be prepared in advance, or simply found around the classroom.) Each pupil in turn estimates the value of the first 'hole', and the quantity is then measured by the group collectively. The player whose estimate was nearest wins the hole and gives the first estimate on the next. At the end of eighteen holes, the player who has won most holes is the winner.

Note

This game can be adapted to any measurable quantities, or to the answers to calculations.

Equations

Age range   11 to 14

Mathematics   Basic arithmetic

Equipment   Two packs of cards, prepared as below

Method of play

This game is essentially a variation of the familiar card game of
Rummy. The two packs of cards are shuffled separately, and
each player is dealt four number cards and three symbol cards;
the rest of each pack is placed face down in the middle of the
table. Each player in turn then
   (i) picks up *either* the top card of the numbers pack *or* the top
       card of the symbols pack *or* the whole of the discard pile;
  (ii) if possible, lays down from his/her hand a valid equation (or
       more than one equation); and
 (iii) discards any one card from his/her hand onto the discard
       pile.

The winner is the first player to empty his/her hand of cards –
this may happen at stage (ii) or stage (iii) above – and each other
player then scores a penalty equal to the number or cards left in
his/her hand.

Preparation

Two ordinary packs are used, each defaced in a different way.
One pack has the normal suit values replaced by numbers (four
each of the numbers from 0 to 12 is suggested), while the other
has arithmetical symbols (possibly eight +, eight –, eight ×, four ÷,
and twenty-four =).

Notes

A valid equation, for the purposes of this game, consists of two
arithmetic expressions (which may be single terms) connected by
an = sign. Thus '$5 = 3 + 2$' and '$3 + 4 = 11 - 4$' and '$6 = 6$' are all valid
equations, but '$1 + 5 = 2 + 4 = 3 + 3$' is not, unless the teacher
decides to allow such formations.

Human Computer

Age range   11 to 14

Mathematics   Binary numbers

Equipment   None

Method of play

Six pupils stand in a line, one behind another, each with the right hand resting on the right shoulder of the person in front. Each pupil is then instructed that whenever he/she feels a tap on the shoulder, the right arm should be raised if it is down or lowered if it is up. The line of pupils now constitutes a simple binary calculator. Another pupil (or the teacher) can enter any number by tapping the appropriate pupil on the shoulder – the pupil at the rear of the line represents 1, the next 2, the next 4, and so on; with six pupils in the line the front pupil will represent 32. The diagram below shows the result of entering 25 (binary 11001) in this way.

| 32 | 16 | 8 | 4 | 2 | 1 |

A second binary number can then be entered similarly, and the 'computer' will show the result of adding the two numbers together. 'Carrying' takes place automatically, because as a pupil lowers his or her arm it inevitably taps the shoulder of the person in front.

Notes

This is most effective if done by one group as a demonstration for the class; the pupils in the line should have their left sides towards the rest of the class. With six pupils as described, results up to 63 can be shown; greater or smaller numbers of pupils will clearly enlarge or restrict the possible range of calculation. (A class of 25 pupils all in line could calculate up to more than 16 million in this way!)

Roulette

Age range 13 upwards

Mathematics Probabilities and odds

Equipment Roulette wheel and ball; betting grid; 'chips'

Method of play

The game of *Roulette* is widely known, but this summary of the
rules may be of help to teachers whose salaries do not allow
frequent visits to Monte Carlo or Las Vegas! Roulette wheels and
other equipment can be obtained through educational suppliers
or from games shops.

One player is appointed as 'croupier' (banker) and is responsible
for spinning the wheel and for receiving and paying out bets.
Each of the other players is given an agreed amount (in chips) to
bet with, and the rest of the chips are placed in the bank.

At the beginning of each round, each player (other than the
banker) may make a bet. (In casinos, players may make more
than one bet if they so wish, but that might well confuse an
amateur croupier.) The possible bets are listed below.

The croupier sets the wheel spinning and throws the ball into the
wheel bowl. Before it begins to settle, the croupier calls *'Rien ne
va plus'* (no more bets), and all players then wait for the ball to
settle in one of the numbered slots. The croupier announces the
winning number and colour (all in French, of course) and pays
off winning bets and collects losing ones.

At the end of an agreed time, pupils are considered to have 'won'
if they have chips to a greater value than those given them at the
start.

Betting layout

The standard European betting table has the form shown
opposite.

P12 M12 D12	NOIR				PAIR				PASSE			
	34	31	28	25	22	19	16	13	10	7	4	1	
	35	32	29	26	23	20	17	14	11	8	5	2	0
	36	33	30	27	24	21	18	15	12	9	6	3	
D12 M12 P12	ROUGE				IMPAIR				MANQUE			

Bets available

Many different bets are allowed; the simplest ones (with the odds paid in each case) are as follows:

Single number (any, including 0)	35 to 1
Rouge (red) or Noir (black)	1 to 1
Pair (even) or Impair (odd)	1 to 1
Manque (1 to 18) or Passe (19 to 36)	1 to 1

Initially, pupils should be restricted to those bets. At a later stage, some additional bets may be introduced:

Première (1 to 12), Moyenne (13 to 24) or Dernière Douzaine (25 to 36)	2 to 1
Colonne (any column)	2 to 1

In addition, the player's original stake is returned if the bet wins.

If the ball lands in 0, then bets on 0 as a single number win (and are paid off at 35–1), and all other bets are lost. This is not strictly according to European practice, but it does happen in the United States and certainly simplifies the croupier's calculations.

Notes

Some teachers may object to any suggestion that we should encourage the practice of gambling. However, if this game is played over any significant period, the built-in bias in favour of the bank (which results not from a biased wheel, but from the fact that the odds are not quite fair) should ensure that pupils tend to lose more often than they win. An added benefit from this game is the practice that it can give in speaking and understanding simple French.

If the table is to be home-made, it may be helpful to note that the 'red' numbers are traditionally numbers 1, 3, 5, 7, 9, 12, 14, 16, 18, 19, 21, 23, 25, 27, 30, 32, 34 and 36; the other numbers (except 0) are black.

The Boiler Problem

Age range   14 upwards

Mathematics   Problem-solving skills

Equipment   Prepared problem details (see below)

Method of play

The group must contain at least four members, and exactly four
is best if this can be arranged. Each member of the group is
given certain information concerning the problem of transporting
a ship's boiler from the factory to the docks, and the group have
to work together to arrive at a solution. What pupils are not told
– and what will probably take them some time to discover – is
that each of them has slightly different information, and that all
the information must be pooled if the problem is to be solved.

Notes

This is just one example of a type of problem frequently posed
on management and leadership courses, and teachers may well
be able to find or invent others. It should be used sparingly,
however – for the age range concerned the mathematics should
be very straightforward, and the lessons to be learned are social
rather than formally mathematical. The teacher should ensure
(probably through group discussion at the end of the game) that
pupils have realised the need to cooperate and to collect
information from as many sources as possible when a problem
has to be solved.

The map and instructions on the five pages following may be
photocopied and/or duplicated as required for use **within the
school**. The map should to tossed casually into the middle of the
group, while a copy of the problem brief is handed to each player
(a different brief for each player, unless there are more than four,
but without any immediately obvious difference).

Teachers may care to note for reference that the only acceptable
route goes via Netherhall Road, St Brendan's Road, Henry
Street, Netherhall Road (again), Smith Street and Blyth Road,
and requires the use of a *Type 1* trailer.

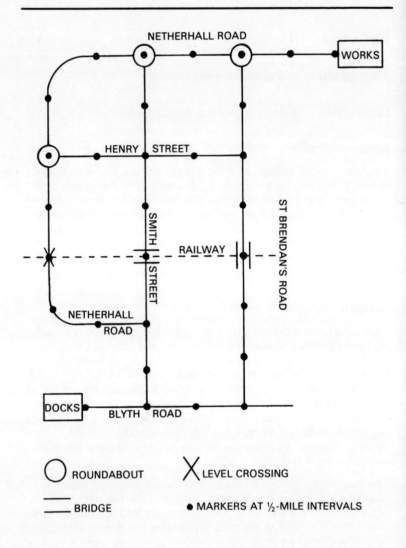

NETHERHALL ROAD

WORKS

HENRY STREET

SMITH STREET

ST BRENDAN'S ROAD

RAILWAY

NETHERHALL
ROAD

DOCKS

BLYTH ROAD

○ ROUNDABOUT

✕ LEVEL CROSSING

— BRIDGE

● MARKERS AT ½-MILE INTERVALS

The Boiler Problem

You are members of the transport department of a private engineering firm. Your firm has just completed the manufacture of a large boiler, which has now to be transported by road from your factory to the docks, as shown on the map. The load must leave the works no earlier than 0500 and must arrive at the dock gate no later than 0730. Your task is to decide how best to accomplish this.

The boiler, which weighs 48 tonnes, will have to be carried on a trailer. Three types of trailer are available: a *Type 1* trailer has eight axles (giving a distributed load of 6 tonnes per axle); a *Type 2* trailer has six axles (8 tonnes per axle); and a *Type 3* trailer has ten axles (4.8 tonnes per axle). This could be important, because there is a strict weight limit of 7 tonnes per axle at the level crossing in Netherhall Road.

Whichever route is chosen, the load will have to pass through at least one roundabout, and this may cause some delay. If the transporter turns left at a roundabout it will need an extra 5 minutes (over and above the ordinary journey time); if it goes straight on it will need an extra 15 minutes; and if it turns right it will need 25 minutes extra.

Which trailer would you recommend, and what route should the load take?

You have twenty minutes.

The Boiler Problem

You are members of the transport department of a private engineering firm. Your firm has just completed the manufacture of a large boiler, which has now to be transported by road from your factory to the docks, as shown on the map. The load must leave the works no earlier than 0500 and must arrive at the dock gate no later than 0730. Your task is to decide how best to accomplish this.

The boiler will have to be carried on a trailer, and three types of trailer are available. A *Type 1* trailer is the fastest, and will allow the load to move at speeds up to 6 mph. *Type 2* trailers have a maximum speed of 3 mph, however, and *Type 3* trailers are limited to just 2 mph.

One major obstacle is the railway line, which must be crossed at some point of the journey. If the load is taken along Smith Street and under the bridge there, an extra 10 minutes will need to be added to the journey time to allow for negotiating the bridge. An alternative route might be via the level crossing on Netherhall Road, but this crossing will be closed between 0600 and 0615 to allow a train to pass through.

Which trailer would you recommend, and what route should the load take?

You have twenty minutes.

The Boiler Problem

You are members of the transport department of a private engineering firm. Your firm has just completed the manufacture of a large boiler, which has now to be transported by road from your factory to the docks, as shown on the map. The load must leave the works no earlier than 0500 and must arrive at the dock gate no later than 0730. Your task is to decide how best to accomplish this.

The boiler will be carried on a trailer, and three types of trailer are available. A *Type 1* trailer stands 80 cm off the ground; when added to the boiler's diameter of 4.20 m this gives an overall height of 5.00 m. A *Type 2* trailer is 50 cm high (overall height 4.70 m); and a *Type 3* trailer is 60 cm high (overall height 4.80 m). This may be important if you intend to use Smith Street, which passes under a railway bridge.

An alternative route without height restrictions would be the one along Netherhall Road. However, the level crossing here will be closed to all traffic between 0600 and 0615, and will in any case take 20 minutes to cross (in addition to normal travelling time). This clearly means that you could not begin to cross it at any time between 0540 and 0615.

Which trailer would you recommend, and what route should the load take?

You have twenty minutes.

The Boiler Problem

You are members of the transport department of a private engineering firm. Your firm has just completed the manufacture of a large boiler, which has now to be transported by road from your factory to the docks, as shown on the map. The load must leave the works no earlier than 0500 and must arrive at the dock gate no later than 0730. Your task is to decide how best to accomplish this.

Various possible routes are available, but each must cross the railway line at some point. The bridge over the railway at St Brendan's Road has a weight limit of 5 tonnes per axle, but is otherwise free of difficulty. The Smith Street bridge under the railway has no weight limit, but does have a height limit of 4.75 m overall, and takes an extra 10 minutes (additional to normal travelling time) to negotiate. The level crossing on Netherhall Road has a weight limit of 7 tonnes per axle.

Turning corners may also present problems because of the length of the boiler. At an ordinary T-junction or crossroads there is no time lost in going straight ahead, but a left or right turn adds 10 minutes to the journey time. (At a roundabout, on the other hand, a left turn adds just 5 minutes while a right turn adds 25 minutes to the journey.)

What route should the load take?

You have twenty minutes.

GAMES FOR THE CLASS

The games in this section are suitable for use with a whole class at once. Most of them, however, can be played by any group of six or more pupils.

Fizz Buzz

Age range   9 to 13

Mathematics   Factors and multiples

Equipment   None

Method of play

Pupils are seated in some clearly understood order – a circle is best. One pupil, chosen at random, then counts 'one', the next 'two', and so on. However, any number which includes the digit 7, or which contains seven as a factor, must not be named but must be replaced by 'buzz'. (For example, the count in the upper forties runs 'forty-five, forty-six, buzz, forty-eight, buzz, fifty, . . .'.) An appropriate (but light-hearted) penalty is imposed on any pupil making a mistake.

That is the game of *Buzz*.

The game of *Fizz* is similar, but uses five instead of seven as a digit or factor, and each of these should be played once or twice for practice before the class moves on to the game of *Fizz Buzz*.

In *Fizz Buzz* both fives and sevens are replaced whenever they occur. Any number which includes both five and seven (e.g. 35, 56, 70) is spoken as 'fizz-buzz'; otherwise 'fizz' or 'buzz' must be used as appropriate.

There are no winners – the game continues as long as the teacher wishes it to.

Variations

The game could obviously be adapted to other numbers, but five and seven are traditional and seem to work quite well. There are several other counting games which might perhaps be regarded as variations on this – pupils learning a foreign language might well be asked to count in that language, for instance.

Another variation is based on a comic sketch, in which Roman soldiers number off – 'Aye', 'Aye-aye', 'Aye-aye-aye', 'Aye-vee', and so on. This may be useful if the class are trying to learn Roman numerals, but the point should be made that although the

Romans *wrote* their numbers like this they *spoke* them as '*unus, duo, tres, quattor,* . . .' (or more probably, when numbering off, as '*primus, secundus, tertius, quartus,* . . .').

Bingo

Age range   9 to 13

Mathematics   Mental arithmetic

Equipment   Bingo cards; Pencils

Method of play

Each pupil begins by making a bingo card similar to the one
shown in the diagram. Fifteen numbers (all between 1 and 90
inclusive) are chosen and written into the boxes in such a way
that there are five numbers on each line. Ideally, each pupil
should have a different set of numbers.

	11		34	41		62		83
6		25	37		54		75	
10	17			45			78	90

The teacher then acts as 'caller', but instead of calling numbers
calls simple mental arithmetic problems. Each pupil works out
the answer to each problem, and crosses off that number if it
appears on his/her card. Suitable prizes can be awarded (if
desired) to the first pupils to obtain:

(a) a 'line' (top, middle or bottom) of five numbers all correctly
    crossed out; and then
(b) a 'canteen sandwich' in which the top and bottom lines are
    crossed out, but there may or may not be anything in the
    middle; and finally
(c) a 'house' with all fifteen numbers crossed out.

Getting Close

Age range   9 to 14

Mathematics   Estimation

Equipment   Blackboard and chalk; pencils and paper; calculator for checking

Method of play

The teacher (or a pupil chosen at random) writes on the board a calculation sufficiently difficult that it cannot reasonably be done mentally. In thirty seconds, each pupil has to estimate the answer and write down his/her estimate; the teacher then works out the actual answer using a calculator, and the pupil whose estimate was nearest wins a point.

Variations

As an alternative, the point can be awarded:

(a) to any estimate that is within a stated percentage of the correct answer, or

(b) to the pupil whose estimate was nearest *but not more than* the actual answer.

Each of these variations calls for slightly different strategy.

Route March

Age range   9 to 14

Mathematics   Map reading; description

Equipment   Maps (one per pupil)

Method of play

Each pupil has a copy of the same map – it can be a small-scale maps such as an Ordnance Survey *Landranger*, or a street map (which is probably better for beginners). One pupil then chooses a route on the map and describes it in terms such as these: 'I start outside the post office, facing north. I take the third turning to the right, then the first to the left, then . . . and then leave the roundabout by the third exit. What is the large building now in front of me?' Other pupils follow this route on their own maps so that they can say where the journey ends.

Notes

For older pupils with a knowledge of scales, the description of the route might well involve distances; it could also involve physical descriptions of the terrain and of relevant landmarks if pupils are familiar (perhaps from geography lessons) with the various conventional signs.

A suitable street map, which may be photocopied and/or duplicated **for use with a class**, is given opposite. Major features are identified by letters, as follows:

A = Town Hall	B = Post office	C = Hospital
D = Cinema	E = Supermarket	F = Police station
G = Bus station	H = Church	I = Bingo hall
J = Garden centre	K = Grand Hotel	L = Garage

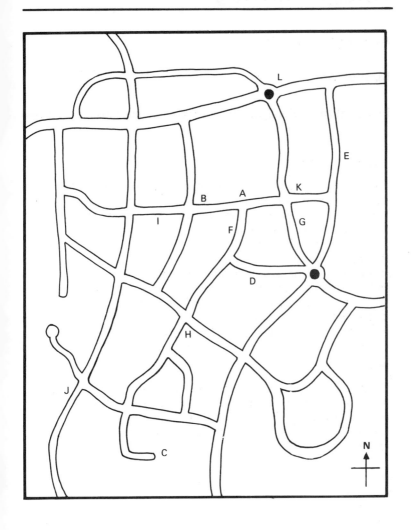

Foreign Currency

Age range 9 to 14

Mathematics Money

Equipment Foreign coins; foreign exchange tables; pencils and paper

Method of play

Each pupil is given one or two foreign coins (not necessarily from the same country) and has to find out as much as possible about it or them before writing a short (half-page) report. The report might include such things as
(a) the country of origin;
(b) the face value;
(c) the equivalent value in British currency;
(d) the colour of the coin;
(e) its design, especially any unusual features;
(f) any inscriptions; and
(g) 'rubbings' of the coin's two faces.

Notes

Teachers or pupils may well bring back small-value foreign coins from their holidays abroad. In addition, many small shopkeepers will occasionally find foreign coins in their change and may be happy to exchange these for British coins of the same size and colour.

Guess the Rule

Age range   9 upwards

Mathematics   As required; also classification

Equipment   Blackboard and chalk (or equivalent)

Method of play

The teacher divides the board into two parts, labelled S and S'
respectively, and secretly decides on a rule for partitioning the
universal set of natural numbers. Pupils in turn then suggest
numbers (initially more or less at random) and the teacher says
whether each number belongs to S or to S', and writes it in the
appropriate part of the board. After four or five numbers have
been written, a pupil may guess at the rule instead of suggesting
a number; the teacher should decide whether a (light-hearted)
penalty is to be imposed for incorrect guesses.

Examples

Suitable partitions (at appropriate ages) might be:
(a) S = {even numbers}, S' = {odd numbers}
(b) S = {numbers greater than 20}, S' = {numbers less than 21}
(c) S = {prime numbers}, S' = {non-prime numbers}

or, using different universal sets,

(d) S = {quadrilaterals}, S' = {other polygons}
(e) S = {linear functions of x}, S' = {non-linear functions}
(f) S = {rational numbers}, S' = {irrational numbers}

Note

Once the class is familiar with this game, a pupil can take the
place of the teacher; however, the teacher should continue to
specify a suitable universal set.

Copy Right

Age range   9 upwards

Mathematics   Geometrical description and drawing

Equipment   Paper and pencils

Method of play

The teacher draws a geometrical diagram and gives it to one pupil. This pupil does not show the diagram to anyone else, but describes it verbally (as clearly and precisely as possible) to the rest of the class. Each of the other pupils draws a diagram from the description given – no interruptions or questions are allowed – and the results are then compared with the original diagram.

Notes

Except with very able pupils, the diagram should be kept very simple – this game is far more difficult than it might seem. The teacher should decide (and should tell the first pupil) whether lengths are to be regarded as significant – initially it is probably easiest to work with shapes only. The sample diagrams following are suggested as being suitable for pupils of average ability at the ages stated.

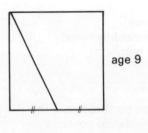

age 9

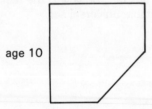

age 10

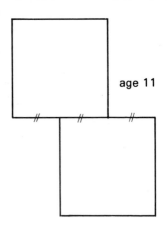

age 11

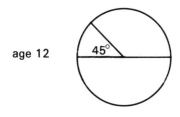

age 12

45°

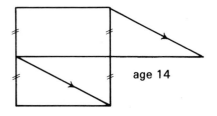

age 14

All the Twos

Age range   11 to 14

Mathematics   Nomenclature

Equipment   None

Method of play

The teacher states a number, and pupils have then to list as
many words as they can which contain a prefix indicating that
number. For example, if the teacher named two, pupils' lists
might include biathlon, bicarbonate, bicentennial, biceps, bicycle,
biennial, bifocal, bigamy, bilateral, binary, binomial, biped,
biplane, biscuit, bivalve, and possibly also dual, duet, duplicate,
and other forms.

Notes

At least in the early stages, the teacher should indicate the
appropriate prefix, and may or may not allow the use of
dictionaries. The most common prefixes in everyday use are as
follows.

```
  1 : uni- or mono-
  2 : bi- (also di- and du-)
  3 : tri- (also ter-)
  4 : quad- (also tetra-)
  5 : quin- or penta-
  6 : sex- or hex- (but beware of irrelevancy!)
  8 : oct-
 10 : deca-
100 : cent-
```

Straight Eights

Age range   11 to 14

Mathematics   Mental arithmetic

Equipment   Calculators; pencil and paper

Method of play

Each pupil has a calculator, and enters a six- or seven-figure number chosen at random. (Each pupil may choose his/her own number, or one number for all the class may be chosen by the teacher.) The teacher then names a digit, and each pupil must calculate mentally what must be added to the number in his/her calculator so that the display will consist entirely of the digit named. For example, if a pupil's calculator showed 3141592 and the teacher named 8, the pupil would add 5747296 so as to obtain 8888888.

Notes

It is suggested that pupils be asked to write down:
(i) their original number, and
(ii) the number they propose to add,
before actually doing the addition. This will both guard against cheating, and also enable the teacher to deal suitably with the bright child who enters 1111111 as the first number every time!

Mathematical Art

Age range   11 to 14

Mathematics   Coordinates; vectors

Equipment   Squared paper and pencils

Method of play

The teacher prepares a diagram containing only straight lines joining points on squared paper. He/she then describes this diagram to the pupils using *either* coordinates *or* vectors in component form, and each pupil draws the diagram from the teacher's instructions.

Variation

When pupils have some experience of this game, they may draw their own diagrams and describe them to one another in similar terms.

Example

The diagram below can be described in terms of either vectors or coordinates, as shown.

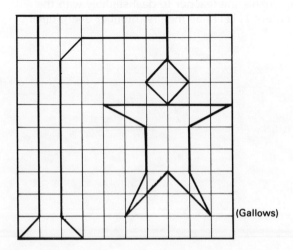

(Gallows)

Coordinate description

Label your grid from 0 to 10 on the x-axis and from 0 to 10 on the y-axis. Then, using straight lines:
join (0,0) to (1,1); join (2,8) to (3,9); join (7,8) to (7,10); join (4,6) to (10,6); join (5,1) to (6,3); join (5,1) to (7,3); join (8,5) to (10,6); join (1,1) to (1,10); join (7,6) to (8,7); join (8,3) to (9,1); join (7,8) to (8,7); join (3,9) to (7,9); – at this point one or two of the sharpest pupils may be able to guess the picture – join (6,3) to (6,5); join (2,1) to (3,0); join (6,7) to (7,6); join (1,10) to (7,10); join (4,6) to (6,5); join (7,3) to (9,1); join (6,7) to (7,8); join (8,3) to (8,5); join (2,1) to (2,8).

Vector description

Begin in the bottom left-hand corner, and draw vectors as follows, each one beginning where the previous one ended.

$$\binom{1}{1};\ \binom{0}{9};\ \binom{6}{0};\ \binom{0}{-2};\ \binom{1}{-1};\ \binom{-1}{-1};\ \binom{3}{0};\ \binom{-2}{-1};\ \binom{0}{-2};$$

$$\binom{1}{-2};\ \binom{-2}{2};\ \binom{-2}{-2};\ \binom{1}{2};\ \binom{0}{2};\ \binom{-2}{1};\ \binom{3}{0};\ \binom{-1}{1};\ \binom{1}{1};$$

$$\binom{0}{1};\ \binom{-4}{0};\ \binom{-1}{-1};\ \binom{0}{-7};\ \binom{1}{-1}.$$

Odd One Out

Age range   11 to 16

Mathematics   Various properties of numbers

Equipment   Blackboard and chalk

Method of play

'Odd one out' questions in tests and quizzes are often criticised on the grounds that more than one answer is possible. In this game, the teacher writes on the board four numbers, chosen more or less at random, and pupils are allowed three minutes to think of a plausible reason why each of the numbers might be the odd one out. For example, if the numbers were 7, 18, 64 and 115, the odd one out could be:

   7 because it is the only prime number, or
  18 because it is the only multiple of 9, or
  64 because it is the only perfect square, or
 115 because it is the only number with a repeated digit.

Notes

As pupils gain experience, the teacher may wish to exclude certain kinds of answer. For example, in the case above, a pupil might answer:

   7 because it is the only number less than ten,
  18 because it is the only number between ten and twenty,
  64 because it is the only number between fifty and a hundred, and
 115 because it is the only number greater than one hundred.

Such an answer is perfectly valid, of course, and deserves full credit when *first* offered; however, if used repeatedly it simply becomes an excuse for not thinking further.

One Hundred

Age range   11 to 16

Mathematics   Mental arithmetic and flexibility

Equipment   Blackboard and chalk

Method of play

The teacher chooses six numbers at random, or asks six pupils
to suggest one number each, and writes them on the blackboard.
Pupils then have one minute in which to combine any or all of
the numbers (using only the operations +, —, × and ÷) to make
exactly 100. (For example, if the numbers given were 21, 5, 3, 38,
26 and 11, a pupil might offer $(5 \times 3) + 21 + 26 + 38$.)

Notes

The time of one minute is suggested as suitable for fairly able
pupils; the teacher may wish to allow longer, although the time
should be clearly stated at the beginning. Alternatively, the
teacher may prefer to stop as soon as the first pupil offers a
correct solution. There is no guarantee, however, that *any* set of
six numbers will have a solution, and so an upper time limit of
five minutes is suggested in any case.

Treasure Hunt

Age range   11 to 16

Mathematics   Coordinates

Equipment   Blackboard and chalk

Method of play

The teacher draws on the board a grid of approximately 10 × 10 squares and labels it with Cartesian coordinates. He/she then secretly chooses one point (the coordinates need not be integral in the case of older pupils) as the hiding place of some buried treasure. Pupils in turn suggest points by giving their coordinates; in each case the teacher gives *either* the distance *or* the direction from the suggested point to the treasure, and marks this information on the board at the appropriate point. This continues until the treasure is found.

Distances

With younger pupils, the distance should be given by the shortest route which follows the lines of the grid (so that (3,5) to (7,3) would give a distance of 6), but once pupils have learned Pythagoras' method (or even a little earlier) the direct distance may be used. The teacher should clearly say which convention he/she is following.

Directions

Older pupils may be given the direction in the form of a bearing (between 0° and 360° to the nearest 10°), but for younger pupils it is probably better to use the ordinary names of the four points. It is quite sufficient for the teacher to say, 'The treasure is to the east of your point,' when in fact it is approximately south-east, as long as this convention is understood.

Function Machine

Age range   12 upwards

Mathematics   Functions

Equipment   Blackboard and chalk

Method of play

The teacher secretly chooses a function defined on the domain of real numbers, or perhaps on a subset of that set. Each pupil in turn then suggests a number to act as argument or 'input', and the teacher writes that number and its image under the function on the blackboard. Once several pairs of numbers have been written, pupils may begin to guess at the function itself.

A pupil who thinks that he/she knows the function may ask the teacher to suggest a number and may then try to give its image. If the pupil's answer is right, he/she is assumed to have guessed the function and is awarded a point accordingly; in this way, the game need not end merely because one pupil has discovered the function, but can continue as long as the teacher feels is desirable.

Notes

Once the class has some experience of this game, the function can be chosen by a pupil instead of by the teacher. In any case, the function chosen must be appropriate to the age and ability of the players – younger pupils should be confined mainly to linear functions with occasional simple powers or functions of the form

$f : x \rightarrow 1$ (x odd)
   $x \rightarrow 0$ (x even)

but older pupils can be offered quadratic or inverse functions, and sixth formers can try to guess reasonably simple logarithmic or trigonometric functions. Even Further Mathematics students might well take some time to guess a function such as

$f : x \rightarrow x$ (x rational)
   $x \rightarrow 0$ (x irrational)

The Drunkard's Walk

Age range   12 upwards

Mathematics   Probability

Equipment   Ordinary dice; grids and counters

Method of play

Each pupil has a grid of nine squares as shown below, and places
a counter on the middle square. He/she then throws an ordinary
die: if it lands 1, 2, 3 or 4 the counter is moved one square to the
left, and if the die lands 5 or 6 the counter is moved one square
to the right. The die is thrown again, and this is repeated until
the counter reaches either the square marked 'Home' or the
square marked 'Dock'.

HOME				PUB				DOCK

Explanation

The game simulates a situation in which a drunk comes out of
the pub at closing time. 400 metres in one direction is his home,
and if he reaches home his wife will drag him in and put him to
bed. 400 metres in the other direction is the dock, into which he is
liable to fall because of his condition. In any five-minute period,
there is a probability $\frac{2}{3}$ that the drunk will walk 100 metres
towards home, and a probability $\frac{1}{3}$ that he will walk 100 metres
towards the dock. We want to find the probability that he does
eventually get home safely.

Notes

If each pupil carries out this simulation independently, their
combined results will represent some 25 or 30 journeys, and it
will be possible to estimate experimentally the overall probability
of the drunk's getting home before he falls into the dock. (If
pupils also count how many times they throw the dice, an
estimate can be made of how long the journey home is likely to

take.) For the game as described above, a theoretical probability of getting home safely is approximately 0.94; most journeys are completed in under 20 throws (100 minutes).

It is possible to vary the probabilities of various moves and to investigate the consequences. Dice are rather limiting in this respect, but with spinners or tables of random numbers all sorts of possibilities emerge. For example, the teacher might assign a probability 0.5 of walking towards home, 0.4 of walking towards the dock, and 0.1 of falling down and going to sleep in the street.

A simulation such as this may well be treated as a game, but in practice this method has extensive uses in various forms of scientific and commercial research.

GAMES FOR THE PLAYGROUND

The few games in this section require rather more space than is to be found in the normal classroom. They can be played out-of-doors, or perhaps in the hall, gymnasium or other large room.

Noughts and Crosses (5)

Age range 9 to 13

Mathematics Strategy; spatial skills

Equipment Chalk

Method of play

The game is basically the same as that described earlier in
Noughts and Crosses (1). The playing grid is chalked on the
ground (or alternatively, nine chairs may be arranged in a solid
square) and two teams of five players each are formed. One
team is 'noughts', the other 'crosses', and one player from each
team in turn walks into the grid and stands in one of the squares.
The first team with three players in line wins the game.

Notes

The teacher may decide whether team members are to be
allowed to consult one another before moving, or whether each
player is to move entirely on his/her own initiative.

Top of the Class

Age range   9 to 13

Mathematics   As required

Equipment   None

Method of play

The pupils stand (or sit) in a line – one end is the 'top' of the class, and the other is the 'bottom'. The teacher moves along the line, asking questions more or less at random; a pupil who answers correctly stays in place, but one who makes a mistake goes to the bottom of the class and other pupils move up one place as necessary. The game continues for as long as the teacher wishes – it can even be played in instalments, with pupils remembering their places in line from day to day.

Notes

Teachers will realise, of course, that this was a standard method of 'teaching' not too many years ago, but now it is so rare that pupils will happily treat it as a game. Refinements (such as a large dunce's cap for the pupil temporarily at the bottom) can be added at the teacher's discretion.

Human Knots

Age range   9 upwards

Mathematics   Topology

Equipment   None

Method of play

All the players – at least twenty of them – stand as close
together as possible, with both arms in the air. The teacher gives
a signal and each player tries to link each of his/her hands with
another, no matter whose. (The teacher may have to give some
assistance if there are two 'free' hands at opposite sides of the
group.) The teacher then gives another signal, and the group
tries (gently) to disentangle itself, *without letting go of any hands.*

Notes

Within reason, the more players the better for this game – the
mathematics is not very deep, but there is fun in plenty especially
with mixed groups. The group may be able to turn itself into a
single circle (perhaps with some members facing outwards and
some inwards), or into two or more circles, linked or separate, or
it may find itself in an unbreakable knot. The game ends when
the players agree that their current formation is the simplest that
can be achieved.

Three from Five

Age range   11 to 16

Mathematics   Strategy; instant arithmetic

Equipment   Chalk, five beanbags (or similar)

Method of play

Three small circles are chalked on the ground, at the corners of
an equilateral triangle with sides of about 10 metres, and a fourth
circle is marked in the centre of the triangle, into which are put
the five beanbags, cotton reels, or other convenient items. The
players are divided into three teams, and each team stands
behind one of the corner circles. One member of each team
plays at a time; other members are allowed to shout advice, but
must remain behind the circles (i.e. outside the triangle) and
must not interfere with the play.

On a signal from the teacher, the playing member of each team
runs forward and picks up one beanbag from the centre circle,
and carries it back to *place* it (not throw or drop) in his/her
team's own circle.The player then goes for another beanbag, and
so on, with the aim of getting three beanbags in his/her team's
circle. When the centre circle is empty – or even before – a
player may take a beanbag from the circle of either of the two
other teams instead. However, a player may carry only *one*
beanbag at a time, and must not throw it; any physical contact
between players should be avoided as far as possible.

The game ends as soon as there are three beanbags
simultaneously in any team's circle. The second member of each
team then becomes the player, and so on until all have had a
turn.

Notes

The game can be adapted to other numbers of teams and
beanbags, but these numbers seem to work best.

Three Ways

Age range   12 to 16

Mathematics   Functions; group theory

Equipment   Chalk

Method of play

A square (just large enough to hold all the players) is chalked in each corner of a rectangular playing area, and all the players start in the same one of these squares. Players then move from square to square according to instructions called by the teacher.

The instruction 'long' means 'move to the square at the other end of the rectangle's long side', the instruction 'short' means 'move to the square at the other end of the rectangle's short side', and the instruction 'cross' means 'move to the square diagonally across the rectangle'. These moves are illustrated in the diagram below.

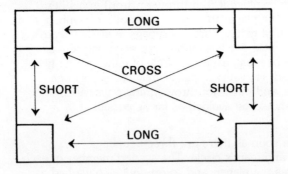

While the players are new to the game, the teacher should use only the simple instructions above, but as soon as they become familiar with the procedure more complex instructions can be given. For example, the instruction 'long cross' means 'move along the rectangle and then diagonally across', and the result of these two in combination is clearly equivalent to a 'short' move. Pupils who can work this out - as they should be encouraged to do - will move directly to the finishing square along the short side of the rectangle. Similarly, 'short cross long' is equivalent to no move at all, and pupils should stay where they are. Suitable penalties can be imposed, at the teacher's discretion, on pupils who go to the wrong squares or who take too long in making up their minds.

Notes

The operations 'short', 'long', 'cross' and 'stay' clearly form a finite group. It is actually a commutative group, and so the order of the operations is not important – this is not of course true of the composition of functions in general.

Mini-orienteering

Age range 11 to 16

Mathematics Bearings and distances

Equipment Markers; magnetic compasses; prepared instructions

Method of play

Nine markers (for example, bottle tops) are labelled from A to I and are set out at the corners of a regular octagon, with one in the middle. The size of this octagon can vary according to the space available, but the radius should be at least 10 metres. A hard surface (e.g. a playground) makes it easier for inexperienced players to spot the markers than does a grassy one.

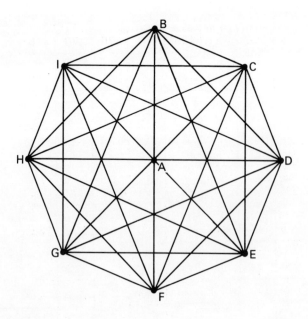

The players (preferably in pairs) are given compasses and instructions leading them (by distance and bearing) along a

course from marker to marker. As they reach each marker, the players note its letter – this will enable them to check later that they have visited the markers in the correct order.

Notes

This game can clearly be extended by the use of more than nine markers, but it then becomes an exercise in the use of compasses rather than in the understanding of bearings. The table below shows, for teachers' convenience, the distances and bearings between nine markers arranged as above. It is assumed that the distance AB is 20 m, and that the direction of AB is due north. (Magnetic variation is ignored, and values are given to the nearest whole metre or degree.)

From \ To	A	B	C	D	E	F	G	H	I
A	—	20 m 0°	20 m 45°	20 m 90°	20 m 135°	20 m 180°	20 m 225°	20 m 270°	20 m 315°
B	20 m 180°	—	15 m 112°	28 m 135°	37 m 158°	40 m 180°	37 m 202°	28 m 225°	15 m 248°
C	20 m 225°	15 m 292°	—	15 m 158°	28 m 180°	37 m 202°	40 m 225°	37 m 248°	28 m 270°
D	20 m 270°	28 m 315°	15 m 338°	—	15 m 202°	28 m 225°	37 m 248°	40 m 270°	37 m 292°
E	20 m 315°	37 m 338°	28 m 0°	15 m 22°	—	15 m 248°	28 m 270°	37 m 292°	40 m 315°
F	20 m 0°	40 m 0°	37 m 22°	28 m 45°	15 m 68°	—	15 m 292°	28 m 315°	37 m 338°
G	20 m 45°	37 m 22°	40 m 45°	37 m 68°	28 m 90°	15 m 112°	—	15 m 338°	28 m 0°
H	20 m 90°	28 m 45°	37 m 68°	40 m 90°	37 m 112°	28 m 135°	15 m 158°	—	15 m 22°
I	20 m 135°	15 m 68°	28 m 90°	37 m 112°	40 m 135°	37 m 158°	28 m 180°	15 m 202°	—

PLAYING GRIDS

The grids on the following pages may be used for playing some of the games described in this book. Any number of copies of the grids may be made by photocopying and/or duplicating for use within a single school or other institution.

S*

*RH

*
BH

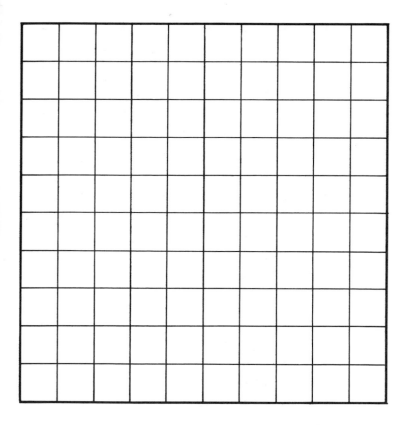

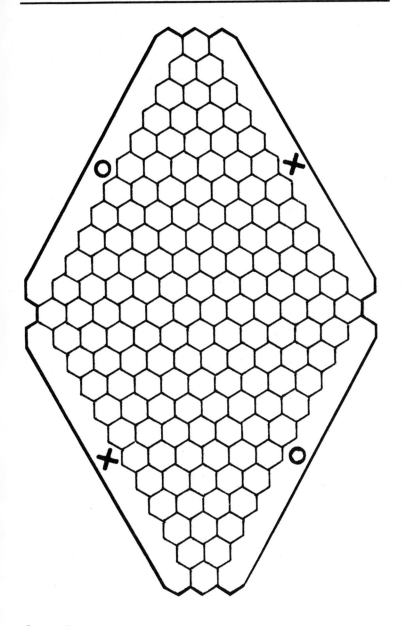

CONTENT INDEX

Quite a number of the games in this book can be adapted to whatever mathematical content the teacher wishes to include. The list below, however, indicates those games of most immediate relevance to particular topics which may appear in the school's scheme of work.